# HEY THAT'S COOL!

**Series Editor:** Colleen Collier
**Researched & Written by:** Hazel Richardson
**Contributors:** Jane Purcell, Sue Curran, Christian Lockley
**Cover & Layout Design:** Alan Shiner


**Published by:**
**LAGOON BOOKS**
**PO BOX 311, KT2 5QW, UK**
**PO BOX 990676, Boston, MA 02199, USA**


**www.lagoongames.com**

**ISBN: 1-902813-47-2**


**© LAGOON BOOKS, 2001**

Printed in Singapore

# HEY THAT'S COOL!

LAGOON
BOOKS

# INTRODUCTION

At last! A book that promises the answers to life, the universe and everything!

How often do you find yourself asking questions such as 'Why is lightning always followed by thunder' and 'What shape is the universe'?
Are you aware that the world is full of amazing phenomena that defy logic and reason, and that many extraordinary occurrences take place on a daily basis without you even realizing?

Well, this fantastic book aims to solve some of these daily riddles for you and will give you knowledge that will astound your friends and family, as well as making you more aware of what goes on around you every day.

# You can use it in two ways:

1. On each 'question' page you will find a score value – if you can figure out the answer to the question without reading the solution on the following page first (no cheating!), you immediately score five points. When you have completed all the questions, simply add up the scores of the ones you have answered correctly and then turn to p.87-88 to find out whether you are really clued up or totally spaced out!

2. However, if you don't want to do the analysis, simply dip into the book at random whenever you feel like finding out an amazing fact, or discovering the answer to a burning question that has been troubling you. It couldn't be simpler!

*Whatever you decide to do, just prepare to be amazed and astounded – the answers to life, the universe and everything are within your grasp.*

# INDEX

# NATURE

## Chapter 1

# NATURE

How can you tell when a storm is happening right over you, and does a full moon really have an adverse effect on human behavior? Here in the Nature chapter, myths will be dispelled and illusions explained. Everything is not how it first appears!

# LIGHT & SOUND

Does thunder always follow lightning?

5 POINTS

3

# LIGHT & SOUND - SOLUTION

Yes, because sound travels more slowly than light.  A flash of lightning heats up the surrounding air, which then rapidly expands. This expansion sets off a massive tidal wave of air, causing a boom of thunder.  You can roughly guess how far away the storm actually is by counting the seconds between a flash of lightning and the thunder that follows.  The shorter the time, the closer the storm.

# BEAR NECESSITIES

What color are polar bears?

5 POINTS

5

# BEAR NECESSITIES - SOLUTION

Amazingly, polar bears are a combination of black, white and transparent!  They are covered in thick transparent fur, but underneath the skin itself is black.

They appear to be white because of the method by which a polar bear retains energy. During the summer, a polar bear can obtain up to 25 per cent of its energy from sunlight. When light hits each hollow hair, it travels down to the black skin, which then absorbs the heat.  All the different colors then fuse together as a white light and bounce back off the fur, giving the impression of a snowy-white polar bear.

# NIGHT VISION

Why are cats better able to see
in the dark than humans?

5 POINTS

7

# NIGHT VISION - SOLUTION

Cats are nocturnal by nature so their vision is designed to accommodate this. Like humans, the pupils of their eyes contract in bright light and expand in the dark, but unlike us, the cat has more optic cells (known as rods), than we do. A further advantage is that cat's eyes reflect light out again, whereas the backs of humans' eyes absorb light. These reflective cells are also the reason why cats' eyes glow in the dark, whereas humans merely bump into things!

# NEITHER HERE NOR THERE

What is a mirage and does it only occur in the desert?

5 POINTS

# NEITHER HERE NOR THERE - SOLUTION

A mirage is the illusion of a pool of water, and is formed by light hitting a layer of hot air above the ground. The light bends and sends out a reflection of sky and clouds, resembling a pool of water. A mirage, therefore, is just as likely to occur on a hot city street as it is in the desert. And in both cases, when you get close to it, it will completely vanish.

# IN A SPIN

How do hurricanes obtain their names?

5 POINTS

# IN A SPIN - SOLUTION

George K Stewart published a novel in 1951 entitled 'Storm', in which the meteorologist hero used women's names for his storms. The idea of storms and women must have become inextricably linked in popular imagination because the following year, real meteorologists officially gave women's names to real storms. This was followed in 1979, by the addition of French, Spanish and popular male names to the list. Currently, a storm is only named when winds hit 39mph and all names are alphabetically chosen in advance over a six-year cycle. Notably, should a hurricane prove particularly destructive, that name is never used again. So, while we will never see another Hurricane Andrew, Camilla, David, Gloria, or Hugo, we might just feel the force of Hurricane Jennifer, Monica or Otis.

# LUNAR LUNACY

Does the full moon really affect human behavior?

**5 POINTS**

13

# LUNAR LUNACY - SOLUTION

Throughout history, lunar power has been vastly overestimated. The full moon, in particular, is the source of a whole host of myths, from the belief that violent behavior is linked to it, to the idea that it affects the birth rate. Astrologers also play on a deeply held belief that the changing moon is somehow linked to our changing moods. Although the moon's gravitational pull does affect the earth in terms of tidal patterns, its pull on the human brain is so tiny that a pillow pushing against your sleeping head exerts a force more than seven trillion times stronger!

# FOREVER FALL

**Why do leaves change color in the Fall?**

5 POINTS

15

# FOREVER FALL - SOLUTION

In Spring and Summer, plants make their food using 'photosynthesis' – a process of breaking down sunlight, water and carbon dioxide. The result of this osmosis is an abundant green chemical called 'chlorophyll', which covers the leaves. As Fall progresses, the plants break down the 'chlorophyll' but can't continue to photosynthesize because of the lack of daylight. Thus the green leaves fade to reveal the true colors of yellow and brown. The brown is made up of tannin wastes in the leaves, whereas any red or purple is due to glucose on the leaves reacting with the light to create a chemical called 'anthocyanins'.

# POLAR PLANET

Is the earth magnetic and, if so,
where does its magnetism come from?

5 POINTS

# POLAR PLANET - SOLUTION

The earth is indeed magnetic and makes its own electricity through the electric currents at its core, with both the liquid and solid part whizzing round at different speeds like a bicycle dynamo. The previously held theory concerning the earth's magnetism was that it was due to the iron contained within its core. This belief was undoubtedly due to the known magnetism of iron, but since a magnet once heated loses its magnetic properties, the iron at the core of the earth would be far too hot to be of any use. Nobody, however, has so far been able to explain why the magnetic fields have sometimes changed direction, so that the magnetic north is suddenly at the South Pole.

# CUT ABOVE

What happens to a worm
if it is cut in half?

5 POINTS

19

# (UT ABOVE - SOLUTION

The theory of the worm regenerating like the villain in 'Terminator' does have some basis in fact. However, it entirely depends on where you cut. Because the worm's brain is at the top half of its body, if you cut far down behind the saddle area, the worm will survive and grow a new tail, whereas the old tail will shrivel up and die. If you cut too close to the brain, however, both halves of the worm will die.

# SPACE

## Chapter 2

# SPACE

Where can electrons travel faster
than the speed of light, and why
doesn't the earth fall through
space? Here in the Space chapter,
Black Holes, the 'Big Bang', and the
shape of the universe itself are
finally revealed.

# 24/SEVEN

Why is a day 24 hours long?

# 24/SEVEN - SOLUTION

The rotation of the earth is controlled by the gravitational pull of the moon on the tides. On average, it takes 24 hours for the earth to make a complete rotation on its axis.

The average day, however, is gradually lengthening. The tides create increasing friction by smashing into cliff faces and moving around the shoreline. As friction is a resistance to motion, two milliseconds are cut from each day every 100 years.

Three billion years ago, a day was only half as long as it is now, but a trillion years from now, a day may well be over a month long.

# SPACE SWELL

What would happen if you fell out
of a spaceship without a spacesuit?

5 POINTS

# SPACE SWELL - SOLUTION

As there is no atmospheric pressure in space, without a spacesuit to mimic the earth's atmospheric pressure your body would quickly swell up and explode. You would also experience your blood turning to boiling foam. This is because the temperature at which liquid boils also depends on atmospheric pressure. For example, on Mount Everest, water boils at 74°C. In space, where there is no pressure, liquids boil at 0°C. Either way, you would end up scattered across the universe!

# GRAVITY GLOBE

Why doesn't the earth fall
through space?

5 POINTS

27

# GRAVITY GLOBE - SOLUTION

The reason we don't fall through space is twofold.  Firstly, 'up' and 'down', as we know it on earth, do not exist in space.  Secondly, rather than falling, the earth is being pulled by the gravitational force of the sun.  The only reason why we aren't pulled to a fiery extinction is because the earth orbits the sun too fast for this to occur.

# SPECK-TACULAR

What is the 'Big Bang' Theory?

5 POINTS

# SPECK-TACULAR - SOLUTION

The 'Big Bang' theory suggests that the universe began about 20 billion years ago, and before that, time did not exist at all. The evidence for this comes from the fact that galaxies are moving away from the earth in every direction, as if they all originated from one central point. This original speck, which scientists refer to as 'a singularity', contained all the energy mass needed to create the universe and when it exploded – the 'Big Bang' – time, space and matter were instantly created. If the 'moving galaxies' theory is correct, there is also the possibility that the universe may one day begin to contract and shrink under the force of gravity, thus returning it to its original 'speck' state.

# STRETCH SPHERE

What happens when an object is
dragged into a Black Hole?

5 POINTS

31

# STRETCH SPHERE - SOLUTION

There are two possible outcomes, depending on the size of the Black Hole.  With a small one, the tremendous force of gravity would stretch the object so strongly that it becomes similar to one long spaghetti string.  Should it tumble into a large Black Hole ('large' meaning one weighing ten million times as much as the sun), it would also be stretched, but not to terminal spaghetti length.  Unfortunately, once it reached the center of the Black Hole, it would be completely crushed anyway.

# WARP SPEED

**Can anything travel faster than the speed of light?**

5 POINTS

# WARP SPEED - SOLUTION

Even if it was technologically possible for a rocket to go faster than the speed of light (ie above 186,291 miles per second), the laws of mass and energy would immediately prevent it from happening. Once the rocket became close to light speed, two things would happen simultaneously. Firstly, less and less rocket energy would be converted into increased speed. And, secondly, more of the energy would be turned into mass. The rocket would become so heavy that an ever-increasing output of power would be required just to keep it up to speed. If it did somehow manage to reach the speed of light, all the energy would instantly be turned into mass, so basically it is impossible.

Having said that, light can travel at much greater speeds in water. This was proved in 1934 by Pavel Cerenkov, who managed to speed up electrons from their average 140,000 miles per second to 160,000 miles per second. For this work, Cerenkov was awarded the Nobel Prize for physics in 1958.

# SEEING IS BELIEVING

What does the universe look like?

5 POINTS

35

# SEEING IS BELIEVING - SOLUTION

The universe is a four-dimensional hyper sphere that changes with time. You could think of it as a multi-layered onion and if you could 'see' the universe at this moment in time, you would be looking right round the outside layer of the onion. The enormity of the universe plus the time quotient, however, means it would actually be impossible to look at it at any given moment. Light from distant stars takes so long to reach us, that when you look into space you are actually looking back in time. And if you could look far enough into space to see the center of the universe – nothing would exist there at all.

# MACHINERY

## Chapter 3

# MACHINERY

What everyday object can cut
through metal, leather, paper,
rubber and plastic, and why was the
QWERTY keyboard set out the way
it is?  Will computers eventually
take over the running of the world?
It is all explained in the revealing
machinery chapter.

# IT'S ALL AROUND

Is there an everyday tool that can cut
through metal, rocks, ceramics, plastic,
rubber, leather and paper?

## 5 POINTS

# IT'S ALL AROUND - SOLUTION

Amazingly, when water is pushed through fine nozzles at up to 1,400m per second, it can be used to cut wood, leather and paper products. Add some abrasives, and water can also slice metal, rock, ceramics and other hard materials.

# COMPUTER KING

Will robots or computers ever
supplant humans?

## 5 POINTS

# COMPUTER KING - SOLUTION

Before plotting an intergalactic takeover, a computer would need a sophisticated ability to think and react creatively. A computer is only as good as its data and the technological ability to give a computer the understanding and common sense of even a small child would be very difficult. If, for example, you told a child that a frog was seen trying on shoes, the child would quickly think it ridiculous. For the computer to come to the same conclusion, it would need specific data about frogs, shoes, shops, and the impossibility of amphibians in footwear. Even to store such a vast amount of information would slow down the computer's basic ability to think.

# AVIATION ANXIETY

How do airplanes take off
and stay in the sky?

5 POINTS

43

# AVIATION ANXIETY - SOLUTION

The wings of an airplane are flat underneath and deliberately curved on top. They also have a curved front and tapered back, which allows air passing over the top to travel faster than the air underneath. This results in the air pressure under the wing being higher than the air pressure over the top, which allows the wings to lift. Thereafter, when a plane is traveling at a constant speed, the lift created by the difference in air pressure is equal to the weight of the plane. The plane's engines counteract air resistance and therefore keep the plane in the sky!

# FIREARM FURNACE

If you fire a gun at a car,
will the gas tank explode?

5 POINTS

45

# FIREARM FURNACE - SOLUTION

Hollywood action movies completely ignore the laws of physics where this matter is concerned.  An ordinary bullet fired through a gas tank would not cause a fire because it's too small, flies for too short a time, and does not give off enough heat.  Were the bullet to flatten on impact, it would heat up a little due to an energy release, and may cause an explosion.

# GROUND FORCE

Could you save yourself in a plummeting
elevator by jumping upwards just before
it hit the ground?

5 POINTS

# GROUND FORCE - SOLUTION

After three seconds of freefall, the elevator would have a downward velocity of 96 feet per second. Since the maximum upward jump humanly possible is only 14 feet per second, you would still be crushed on impact at a velocity of 82 feet per second. Even if you wore turbo-charged boots that could shoot you up at 96 feet per second, the acceleration would still crush you.

# PLANE POWER

If a gun were fired through the window of a flying aircraft, would the passengers be in danger of being sucked out?

5 POINTS

# PLANE POWER - SOLUTION

A small hole in an aircraft window would not automatically depressurize the cabin. Even though airplanes are pressurized, they are not airtight and the pressure inside is actually balanced by pumping in air. There have, in fact, been incidents of whole doors being blown off mid-flight without any fatalities. In 1988, an Aloha Airlines Boeing 737 had a large chunk of the plane roof ripped off at 24,000 feet. One flight attendant was swept out, but the other passengers remained in their seats and the plane landed safely.

# KEYBOARD QUERY

Why was the **QWERTY** keyboard invented?

## 5 POINTS

# KEYBOARD QUERY - SOLUTION

The **QWERTY** keyboard is deliberately designed to have the most commonly used letters as far apart on the keyboard as possible. When the typewriter was first invented in 1829, the keys were laid out in alphabetical order, but as the typist became faster, the keys would constantly jam. The **QWERTY** format is thus meant to slow the typist down. However, the fact that many modern typists can tap up to 120 words per minute demonstrates that the designers did not fully succeed!

# HOME

## Chapter 4

# HOME

Why does water go down the plughole clockwise, and why do you cry when you chop onions? These things affect us on a daily basis – do you have the answers? Investigate further in the Home chapter.

# DOWNWARD SPIRAL

Why does water appear to go down
the plughole in a clockwise direction?

5 POINTS

55

# DOWNWARD SPIRAL - SOLUTION

Water may appear to be swirling clockwise down the plughole but it is actually an illusion. An earthly pulling power is at work – the Coriolis force – that is responsible for turning the world on its axis and also 'pulling' water and air. Coriolis, however, is quite a weak force and can only cause water and air to spin clockwise if there are massive quantities of it, such as in the atmosphere or in the oceans. So there isn't actually enough water in your bath or sink to swirl entirely in the same direction.

# CRY BABY

Why do tears come to your eyes
when you chop onions?

5 POINTS

# CRY BABY - SOLUTION

Onions contain a nasty chemical gas called 'propennyl sulphuric acid' that is released as soon as you break open its cells. This chemical is released when the onion is chopped and immediately reacts with your eyes when it hits your eyeballs. A weak acid is formed that irritates them and makes tears come to the surface. However, one way to avoid crying, is to chop onions underwater as this prevents the gas from reaching your face.

# METAL MAYHEM

What happens if you put metal objects into a microwave?

5 POINTS

# METAL MAYHEM - SOLUTION

Unbelievably, there is a certain type of metal you can put into the microwave without causing horror movie effects. When a ready-prepared meal is placed in the microwave, it usually has a piece of paperboard as a cover. After you remove the paperboard, you can see a metalized film underneath. This actually absorbs microwaves, turning them into heat energy which helps to brown your food. What you shouldn't do, however, is put a thick metal tray into the microwave. If you do, microwaves will crash against the metal causing huge arcing sparks of electricity to be thrown off – producing something similar to a lightning storm in your oven!

# DENTAL DILEMMA

Why don't the stripes in toothpaste
ever mix?

5 POINTS

# DENTAL DILEMMA - SOLUTION

Toothpaste is deliberately made to a consistency that makes it stiff enough not to blend, but soft enough to be squeezed out of the tube. Each color is made and pumped into the toothpaste tube separately, through its own nozzle. This means that the stripes are kept separate from the first squeeze to the last. If, however, you have too much time on your hands, it is possible to mix up the stripes if you really twist and scrunch up the tube!

# STATIC STATISTICS

Why is hair more flyaway in Winter than Summer?

5 POINTS

# STATIC STATISTICS - SOLUTION

Hair is more likely to go **AWOL** in Winter because the drier air causes excess static electricity. Electricity itself consists of negatively charged electrons that move around in the atmosphere. If you take off your hat on a cold day, the negative electrons move to your hat, leaving behind a positive charge on your hair. As positive and negative electrons repel each other, your hair stands on end. Summer air, however, is much more humid, and the water droplets in the atmosphere help the electrons move away faster. This means that hat or no hat, you don't build up a 'repellent' electrical charge and therefore have fewer wild hair days.

# EASILY LEAD

How does lead get slotted into a pencil?

5 POINTS

# EASILY LEAD - SOLUTION

Manufacturers used to manually bore a hole down the center of each pencil and slide a rod of lead inside. Today, however, mass production means that pencils are produced in blocks of eight slats of cedar wood. A machine cuts eight grooves, into which is slotted a rod. Although we still refer to 'lead' pencils, the 'lead' is actually a combination of graphite, clay and water, heated at high temperatures and pressed into thin rods. Once these rods are in place, a second slat is glued on top and these are fed through another machine that cuts them into eight separate pencils. The glued seam where the two slats are joined is then sanded down and painted, giving the finished pencil the illusion of a seamless, solid structure.

# LIGHTWEIGHT

Does it make a difference where you keep weighing scales?

5 POINTS

67

# LIGHTWEIGHT - SOLUTION

The further apart an object is from earth, the weaker gravity becomes.  Therefore, you will weigh slightly less on the upper storey of your house than you will on the ground floor.
But for a really gratifying weight loss on a set of standard scales, you would need to weigh yourself on the roof of the **CNN** building!

# EXPERIMENTS

## Chapter 5

# EXPERIMENTS

How can you squeeze an egg through the neck of a bottle, and how can you find the iron that is supposed to be in your breakfast cereal? Now that you've read all the questions and answers, learn a few experiments that defy logic and will astound your family and friends in the Experiments chapter.

# MOVING MONEY

How to move a coin without touching it

5 POINTS

# MOVING MONEY - SOLUTION

Take an empty glass bottle and place a coin on its rim. Seal the edges of the coin with a few drops of water or cooking oil and wrap your hands round the bottle. After a few moments, the heat from your hands will warm the air inside it. Hot air expands and tries to escape the bottle, thereby making the coin move.

# HOT AIR

**How to blow up a balloon without blowing**

## 5 POINTS

# HOT AIR - SOLUTION

Fill a bottle with hot water for a few minutes.
Then empty it and immediately fasten a balloon
over the neck. Then place the bottle into a
bowl of iced water.  As soon as the bottle is
placed into this, the warm air in the bottle
cools and contracts, forcing outside air to be
sucked into the balloon which then
automatically inflates.

# AIR POWER

## How to break wood with only the power of air

# AIR POWER - SOLUTION

This experiment demonstrates the amount of atmospheric pressure that daily pushes down on us.  On a table, place a thin piece of wood, such as a ruler, with just less than half of it sticking over the side.  Then place a sheet of newspaper over the ruler flat on the table, smoothing it out so that there is as little air as possible underneath.  Quickly hit the part of the ruler hanging off the table.  A whole sheet of newspaper has nearly 9,300 pounds of air above it and when you hit the ruler really fast, you are attempting to lift 9,300 air pounds. With the newspaper so flat, the air around the paper cannot get underneath the paper quickly enough.  Therefore, if you can hit it with enough speed, it will break.

# NO YOKE!

How to squeeze an egg into a bottle

## 5 POINTS

# NO YOKE! - SOLUTION

Soak an unshelled, boiled egg in vinegar overnight and then dry it off.  Take a bottle that's big enough for the egg to sit in but not to fall through.  Gently place the egg in the mouth of the bottle.  The acid vinegar will have broken down the hard calcium carbonate part of the shell, leaving the spongier connective part intact.  Squeeze the sides of the egg and it will slide, unbroken, into the bottle.

# BLADE BALANCE

How to lift a jar of rice with only a knife

## 5 POINTS

# BLADE BALANCE - SOLUTION

This experiment is another simple example of how gravity can be defied. Fill a plastic jar with rice and jab a knife into it ten times. The rice will then settle, so keep adding rice until the jar is packed. Then jab the knife into the jar once again. The rice will now be so densely packed that it will press against the knife blade with enough force to allow you to lift the entire jar.

# LIGHT ELECTRIC

## How to make lightning

### 5 POINTS

# LIGHT ELECTRIC - SOLUTION

Create instant electricity lightning by taking a large metal baking tray and placing it on a thick sheet of plastic, or a garbage bag. Have a small metal object, such as a key, close by. Stick a large amount of Pleistocene into the middle of the tray. Hold onto the Pleistocene and rub the tray round and round on the plastic. Lifting the tray up by the Pleistocene, hold the metal object close to a corner of the tray. A huge spark will immediately jump from it.

# BRIGHT SPARKS

**How to power a light bulb with a balloon**

## 5 POINTS

# BRIGHT SPARKS - SOLUTION

Cover a fluorescent light bulb with sticky tape to minimize the possibility of injury should it break.  Then, wearing your woolliest sweater, blow up a balloon in the darkest room of the house.  Charge the balloon with static electricity by rubbing it vigorously on your sweater.  When you touch the balloon to the bulb, small sparks will instantly appear.

# IRON MAN

How to find the iron in your cereal

5 POINTS

# IRON MAN - SOLUTION

This experiment shows how much iron you actually consume with your cereal. Tape a small magnet onto the end of a wooden spoon. Place a whole box of iron-enriched bran into a large bowl and crush it up. Once the cereal is pulverized, add enough water to make a thin soup. Then stir the cereal soup with the spoon for a few minutes. When you look at the spoon, you will find small pieces of iron attached to the magnet.

# SCORING ANALYSIS

## MAXIMUM POINTS = 190

## 0 – 50

Do you really live on this planet?
If so, you must be walking around each day with your eyes firmly shut! Instead of putting your feet up in front of the television to watch another game show or sports event, how about watching the latest cutting-edge documentary on space exploration or technological advancements?
There is a whole world out there – if you understand it, you will enjoy it even more!

## 55 – 100

You obviously know a little bit – but not that much!
Why don't you take the time to get a bit more clued-up by investigating matters even further? – there is a whole wealth of information in books and magazines at your local library. Why settle for the basic details when you could become a world authority!

# SCORING ANALYSIS

## 105 – 160

We're impressed – you either have an analytical brain and have worked out the answers step-by-step, or else you enjoy learning about how things work and the world in general. You are certainly clued-up, however, there is more to learn – how about subscribing to a monthly periodical or digest on your personal favorite subject? The next Nobel Prize could have your name on it.

## 165 – 190

Well, you either cheated or are truly a genius! Congratulations! You are completely clued-up and very in tune with life, the universe and everything. If we publish another book in this series, we may well ask you to do all the research!

# LAGOON WEB SITE

**Games, Books, Puzzles and Gizmos**

Visit the Lagoon Web Site to view a staggering
range of fantastic games, puzzles
and books to suit all.

# www.lagoongames.com

89

# OTHER LAGOON TITLES

## BRAIN-BOOSTING PUZZLE BOOKS

**Brain-Boosting Cryptic Puzzles**
(1-902813-21-9)

**Brain-Boosting Visual Logic Puzzles**
(1-902813-20-0)

**Brain-Boosting Lateral Thinking Puzzles**
(1-902813-22-7)

## MIND-BENDING PUZZLE BOOKS

**Mind-Bending Lateral Thinking Puzzles**
(1-89971-206-2)

**More Mind-Bending Lateral Thinking Puzzles**
(1-89971-219-4)

**Mind-Bending Challenging Optical Puzzles**
(1-89971-269-0)

**Mind-Bending Maze Puzzles**
(1-89971-272-0)

**Mind-Bending Conundrums and Puzzles**
(1-89971-203-8)

**Mind-Bending Lateral Thinking Puzzles by Des MacHale**
(1-89971-223-2)

**Mind-Bending Classic Logic Puzzles**
(1-89971-218-6)

**Mind-Bending Challenging Logic Puzzles**
(1-89971-224-0)